A Pocketful of Tunes

C instruments edition

For Flute, Oboe, Violin, Recorder
plus chords for Guitar & Keyboard

Kevin Mayhew

We hope you enjoy A *Pocketful of Tunes* for C instruments.
Further copies of this and the other books in the series
are available from your local music shop.

In case of difficulty, please contact the publisher direct:

The Sales Department
KEVIN MAYHEW LTD
Rattlesden
Bury St Edmunds
Suffolk IP30 0SZ

Phone 01449 737978
Fax 01449 737834

Please ask for our complete catalogue of outstanding Instrumental Music.

First published in Great Britain in 1995 by Kevin Mayhew Ltd

© Copyright 1995 Kevin Mayhew Ltd

ISBN 0 86209 717 7
Catalogue No: 3611173

Cover design by Neil Pinchbeck
Music edited and arranged by Donald Thomson
Music Setting: Daniel Kelly

Printed and bound in Great Britain

Contents

A life on the ocean wave	14	New World Symphony (2nd Movement)	37
Abide with me	48	Nobody knows the trouble I see	19
Air from Suite No 3	7	O for the wings of a dove	42
All the nice girls love a sailor	9	O my beloved father	43
All through the night	42	O Sole Mio	12
Amazing Grace	8	Ode to joy	11
Auld Lang Syne	15	Oh dear, what can the matter be?	25
Ave verum corpus	38	One fine day from 'Madame Butterfly'	21
Blow the wind southerly	10	Over the sea to Skye	5
Blue Danube Waltz	46	Panis angelicus	22
Bobby Shaftoe	21	Parade of the Tin Soldiers	28
Caprice	21	Pavane	43
Charlie is my darling	44	Polly-wolly-doodle	44
Clementine	23	Prelude	33
Cockles and Mussels	14	Promenade	41
Country Gardens	31	Radetzky March	39
Daddy wouldn't buy me a bow-wow	30	Romanza	17
Daisy, Daisy	6	Rondo from Horn Concerto K495	19
Dance of the Hours	25	Rule, Britannia	10
Danny Boy	26	Sailors' Hornpipe	31
Down by the riverside	37	Scarborough Fair	12
Early one morning	34	Scène from 'Swan Lake'	15
Eine Kleine Nachtmusik	29	Shaker song	18
For he's a jolly good fellow	46	Sheep may safely graze	38
Für Elise	26	Spring from 'The Four Seasons'	6
Galop	36	Swing low	48
Glory, glory hallelujah	30	The Ash Grove	41
Goodnight ladies	48	The Blue Bell of Scotland	22
Greensleeves	9	The Can Can	29
Hungarian Dance No 5	23	The Drunken Sailor	11
I do like to be beside the seaside	33	The Entertainer	20
I'll take you home again, Kathleen	35	The Floral Dance	45
It's a long way to Tipperary	47	The flowers that bloom in the spring	13
Jerusalem	8	The Keel Row	12
John Peel	35	The Lincolnshire Poacher	42
Kum ba yah	6	The Trout Quintet	32
La Cucaracha	25	The Yellow Rose of Texas	16
La Donna è Mobile	45	Theme from Symphony No 1 (Brahms)	28
Largo	32	Theme from Violin Concerto (Beethoven)	36
Lilliburlero	32	Toreador's song from 'Carmen'	24
Little brown jug	17	Trumpet Tune	5
Loch Lomond	47	Trumpet Voluntary	18
Lullaby	13	Valse Lente from 'Coppélia'	36
Mango walk	27	Waltz	40
Men of Harlech	24	Waltz from 'Die Fledermaus'	40
Michael, row the boat ashore	8	Waltzing Matilda	7
Morning has broken	30	When the saints go marching in	44
My bonnie lies over the ocean	39	Wi' a hundred pipers	16
My Grandfather's clock	34	William Tell Overture	20
Nessun Dorma	16	Ye banks and braes	27

Arranger's Note

The tunes in this book have been arranged for C instruments. Although the melody line may be played alone, accompanying chords for use by keyboard or guitar players have also been provided. Where necessary, an easier version for guitar using a capo is shown below the keyboard chords.

OVER THE SEA TO SKYE

Traditional Scottish Melody

TRUMPET TUNE

Henry Purcell

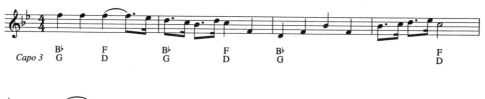

SPRING from 'THE FOUR SEASONS'
Antonio Vivaldi

KUM BA YAH
Traditional Angolan Melody

DAISY, DAISY
Harry Dacre

AIR from SUITE NO 3

Johann Sebastian Bach

WALTZING MATILDA

Marie Cowan

MICHAEL, ROW THE BOAT ASHORE
Traditional Melody

JERUSALEM
Charles Hubert Parry

AMAZING GRACE
Traditional American Melody

ALL THE NICE GIRLS LOVE A SAILOR

A J Mills and Bennett Scott

GREENSLEEVES

Anonymous 17th Century Melody

RULE, BRITANNIA
Thomas Arne

BLOW THE WIND SOUTHERLY
Traditional English Melody

THE DRUNKEN SAILOR
Sea Shanty

ODE TO JOY
Ludwig van Beethoven

THE KEEL ROW
Traditional English Melody

— G   C   G   D   G   C   G   D   G

G   C   G   D   G   C   G   D7   G

O SOLE MIO
Eduardo di Capua

—   C   G7

C   Fm

C   G7   C

SCARBOROUGH FAIR
Traditional English Melody

Em   B   Em   A   Em

Bm   G   D   Em   Am   Bm   Em

THE FLOWERS THAT BLOOM IN THE SPRING

Arthur Sullivan

LULLABY

Johannes Brahms

A LIFE ON THE OCEAN WAVE

Henry Russell

COCKLES AND MUSSELS

Traditional Irish Melody

14

SCÈNE from 'SWAN LAKE'

Peter Ilyich Tchaikovsky

AULD LANG SYNE

Traditional Scottish Melody

15

THE YELLOW ROSE OF TEXAS

Traditional American Melody

NESSUN DORMA

Giacomo Puccini

WI' A HUNDRED PIPERS

Traditional Scottish Melody

ROMANZA
Anon

LITTLE BROWN JUG
R A Eastburn

SHAKER SONG
Traditional American Melody

TRUMPET VOLUNTARY
Jeremiah Clarke

RONDO from HORN CONCERTO K495

Wolfgang Amadeus Mozart

NOBODY KNOWS THE TROUBLE I SEE

Spiritual

WILLIAM TELL OVERTURE

Gioachino Rossini

THE ENTERTAINER

Scott Joplin

CAPRICE
Nicolo Paganini

ONE FINE DAY from 'MADAME BUTTERFLY'
Giacomo Puccini

BOBBY SHAFTOE
Sea Shanty

PANIS ANGELICUS
César Franck

THE BLUE BELL OF SCOTLAND
Traditional Scottish Melody

HUNGARIAN DANCE NO 5
Johannes Brahms

CLEMENTINE
Percy Montrose

MEN OF HARLECH
Traditional Welsh Melody

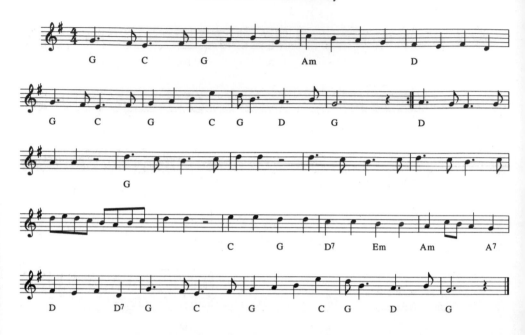

TOREADOR'S SONG from 'CARMEN'
Georges Bizet

DANCE OF THE HOURS
Amilcare Ponchielli

LA CUCARACHA
Traditional Mexican Melody

OH DEAR, WHAT CAN THE MATTER BE?
Traditional Melody

DANNY BOY
Traditional Irish Melody

FÜR ELISE
Ludwig van Beethoven

YE BANKS AND BRAES
Traditional Scottish Melody

MANGO WALK
Jamaican Folk Song

27

PARADE OF THE TIN SOLDIERS

Leon Jessel

THEME from SYMPHONY NO 1

Johannes Brahms

EINE KLEINE NACHTMUSIK
Wolfgang Amadeus Mozart

THE CAN CAN
Jacques Offenbach

GLORY, GLORY HALLELUJAH
William Stäffe

MORNING HAS BROKEN
Traditional Gaelic Melody

DADDY WOULDN'T BUY ME A BOW-WOW
Joseph Tabrar

SAILORS' HORNPIPE
Sea Shanty

COUNTRY GARDENS
Traditional English Melody

LILLIBURLERO
Traditional English Melody

LARGO
George Frideric Handel

THE TROUT QUINTET
Franz Schubert

I DO LIKE TO BE BESIDE THE SEASIDE
John Glover-Kind

PRELUDE
Frédéric Chopin

MY GRANDFATHER'S CLOCK
Henry Clay Work

EARLY ONE MORNING
Traditional English Melody

I'LL TAKE YOU HOME AGAIN, KATHLEEN

Thomas Westendorf

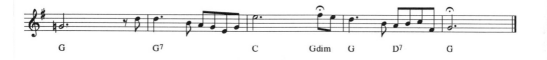

JOHN PEEL

Traditional English Melody

THEME from VIOLIN CONCERTO
Ludwig van Beethoven

VALSE LENTE from 'COPPÉLIA'
Léo Delibes

GALOP
Jacques Offenbach

DOWN BY THE RIVERSIDE

Spiritual

NEW WORLD SYMPHONY (2nd Movement)

Antonín Dvořák

SHEEP MAY SAFELY GRAZE
Johann Sebastian Bach

AVE VERUM CORPUS
Wolfgang Amadeus Mozart

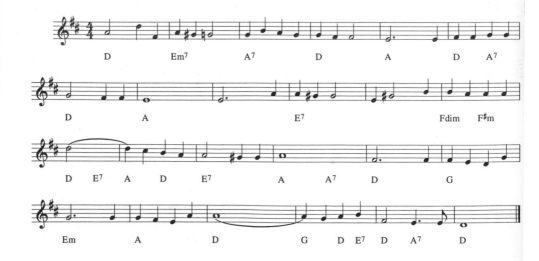

RADETZKY MARCH
Johann Strauss

Capo 3

MY BONNIE LIES OVER THE OCEAN
Traditional Melody

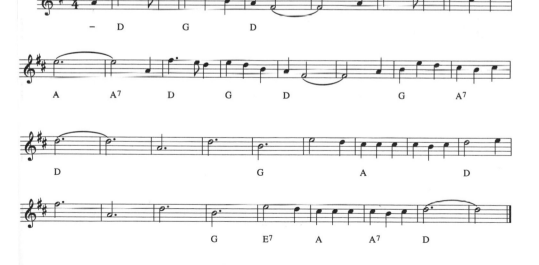

WALTZ
Johannes Brahms

Capo 3

D		G	D	Bm		C#7
F		B♭	F	Dm		E7

rall.

F#m	A7	D	D7	G	E7	A7
Am	C7	F	F7	B♭	G7	C7

a tempo

D		G	D	Bm		D	A7	D
F		B♭	F	Dm		F	C7	F

WALTZ from 'DIE FLEDERMAUS'
Johann Strauss

—   Am   G   D

1. D7   G   *2.* D7   G   *Fine*   D

A7   D

D.C.

Em   E7   A   A7   D

THE ASH GROVE
Traditional Welsh Melody

PROMENADE from
'PICTURES AT AN EXHIBITION'
Modest Musorgsky

ALL THROUGH THE NIGHT
Traditional Welsh Melody

O FOR THE WINGS OF A DOVE
Felix Mendelssohn

THE LINCOLNSHIRE POACHER
Traditional English Melody

O MY BELOVED FATHER

Giacomo Puccini

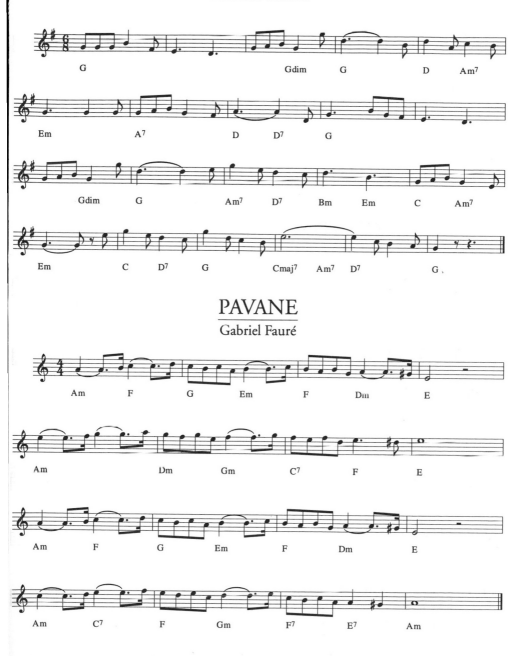

PAVANE

Gabriel Fauré

POLLY-WOLLY-DOODLE

Traditional American Melody

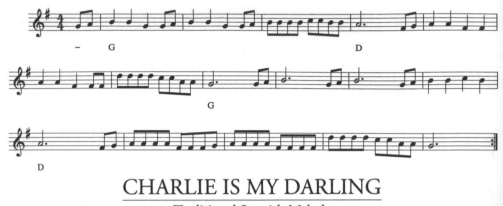

CHARLIE IS MY DARLING

Traditional Scottish Melody

WHEN THE SAINTS GO MARCHING IN

Spiritual

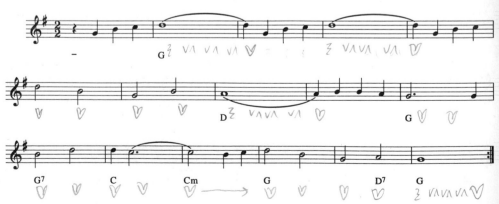

44

LA DONNA È MOBILE

Giuseppe Verdi

THE FLORAL DANCE

Traditional English Melody

BLUE DANUBE WALTZ
Johann Strauss

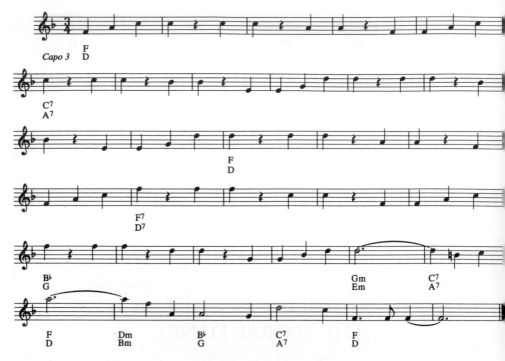

FOR HE'S A JOLLY GOOD FELLOW
Traditional English Melody

IT'S A LONG WAY TO TIPPERARY

Jack Judge and Harry Williams

LOCH LOMOND

Traditional Scottish Melody

ABIDE WITH ME
William Henry Monk

SWING LOW
Spiritual

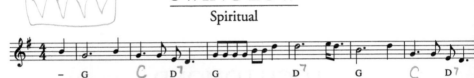

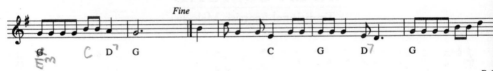

GOODNIGHT, LADIES
Traditional English Melody